# Spelling Made Easy

Key Stage 2

**AGES 7-8**

**Author** Huw Thomas

LOND···  ···OURNE · DELHI

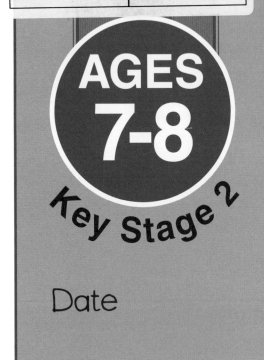

**AGES 7-8**

Key Stage 2

# Certificate

Congratulations to

............................................................
(write your name here)

for successfully

finishing this book.

## GOOD JOB!

You're a star.

Date

............................

**DK**

LONDON, NEW YORK, MUNICH,
MELBOURNE, and DELHI

**DK UK**
**Editor** Jolyon Goddard
**Managing Art Editor** Richard Czapnik
**Producer, Pre-production** Francesca Wardell
**Producer** Christine Ni

**DK Delhi**
**Editor** Rohini Deb
**Art Editor** Dheeraj Arora
**Assistant Art Editor** Kanika Kalra
**DTP Designer** Anita Yadav
**Managing Editor** Soma B. Chowdhury

Published in Great Britain in 2014 by Dorling Kindersley Limited
80 Strand, London WC2R 0RL

Copyright © 2014 Dorling Kindersley Limited
A Penguin Random House Company
10 9 8 7 6 5 4 3 2 1
001—196493—July/2014

A CIP catalogue record for this book is available from the British Library.
ISBN 978-1-4093-4945-7

Printed and bound in China by L. Rex Printing Co., Ltd.

Discover more at
**www.dk.com**

# Contents

This chart lists all of the topics in the book. When you complete each page, stick a star in the correct box. When you've finished the book, sign and date the certificate.

| Page | Topic | Star | Page | Topic | Star | Page | Topic | Star |
|---|---|---|---|---|---|---|---|---|
| 4 | Find the plurals | ☆ | 14 | Rhyming pairs | ☆ | 24 | What are they doing? | ☆ |
| 5 | Find the rule | ☆ | 15 | Rhyme time | ☆ | 25 | Adjectives with "y" endings | ☆ |
| 6 | Singular to plural | ☆ | 16 | Blends and ends | ☆ | 26 | Adverbs ending in "ly" | ☆ |
| 7 | Making plurals | ☆ | 17 | Silent letters | ☆ | 27 | The suffixes "er" and "est" | ☆ |
| 8 | The prefixes "un" and "dis" | ☆ | 18 | The "le" crossword | ☆ | 28 | Find the rule | ☆ |
| 9 | The prefix "pre" | ☆ | 19 | Words in words | ☆ | 29 | The suffixes "ful" and "less" | ☆ |
| 10 | The prefix "de" | ☆ | 20 | Spelling practice | ☆ | 30 | More about "ful" and "less" | ☆ |
| 11 | Recycling words | ☆ | 21 | Compound words | ☆ | 31 | Word-maker | ☆ |
| 12 | Secret message | ☆ | 22 | Find the rule | ☆ | 32 | More spelling practice | ☆ |
| 13 | Contractions | ☆ | 23 | Add "ing" | ☆ | 33 | Answer section with parents' notes and glossary | |

When there is one of something, we say it is **singular**.
For example: Tom had one **apple** for breakfast.

When there is more than one of something, we say it is **plural**.
For example: Tom had two **apples** for breakfast.

apple

apples

Join each of the singular words below to its plural. One has been done for you.

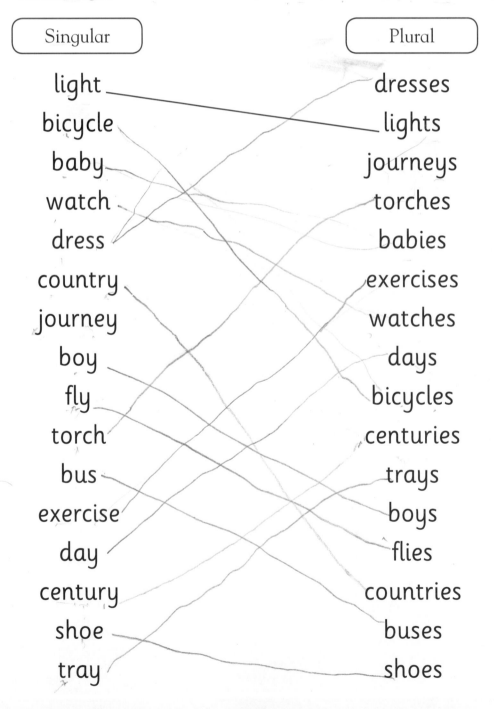

| Singular | Plural |
| --- | --- |
| light | dresses |
| bicycle | lights |
| baby | journeys |
| watch | torches |
| dress | babies |
| country | exercises |
| journey | watches |
| boy | days |
| fly | bicycles |
| torch | centuries |
| bus | trays |
| exercise | boys |
| day | flies |
| century | countries |
| shoe | buses |
| tray | shoes |

The **plurals** of words ending in **soft sounds**, such as **s**, **ss**, **sh**, **ch** and **x** have **es** at the end.
For example:  box ⟶ boxes

Make plurals of words ending in a **vowel** and **y** by adding **s**.
For example:  toy ⟶ toys

For plurals of words ending in a **consonant** and **y**, change the **y** to **i** and add **es**.
For example:  jelly ⟶ jellies

Look at the word endings in the first column below. In the second column, write out the rule for making plurals for each group and then use it to make the words in the last column plural (the first rule and one of the examples have been done for you).

fishes?  fishyes?  fishies?  fish?

| Word endings | The rules | Examples |
|---|---|---|
| **s**, **ss**, **sh**, **ch** and **x** | Add **es** to the end. ............... <br> ......................................... <br> ......................................... | dish ..........dishes.......... <br> match ........................... <br> fox ............................. |
| A vowel and **y** | ......................................... <br> ......................................... <br> ......................................... | donkey ......................... <br> boy ............................. <br> way ............................. |
| A consonant and **y** | ......................................... <br> ......................................... <br> ......................................... | granny ......................... <br> potty ........................... <br> party ........................... |

A **singular** word describes just one thing, such as one car, but a **plural** can be any amount greater than one, such as two, fifty or one million cars.

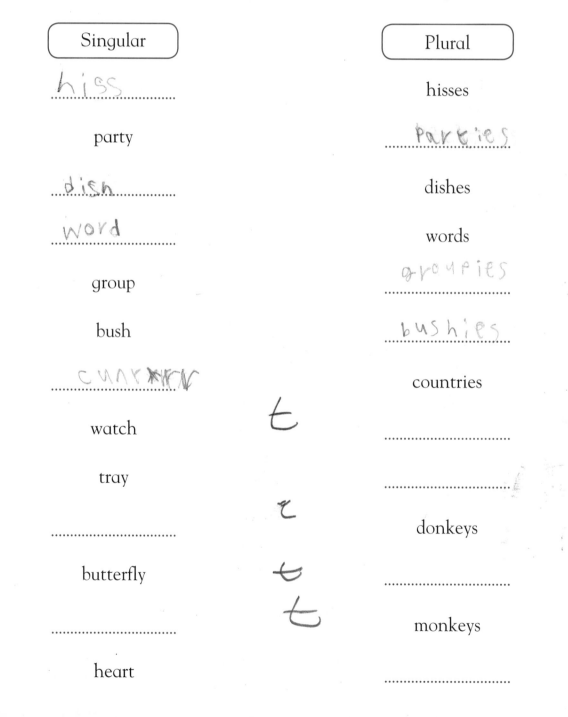

car                              cars

Change the singular words to plural and the plural words to singular.

| Singular | Plural |
|---|---|
| hiss | hisses |
| party | parties |
| dish | dishes |
| word | words |
| group | groupies |
| bush | bushies |
| cuntrern | countries |
| watch | |
| tray | |
| | donkeys |
| butterfly | |
| | monkeys |
| heart | |

To make **singular** nouns into **plurals**, the word endings are changed.

For most nouns, just add **s**. For example:  cat  →  cats

For nouns ending in soft sounds, such as
**s, ss, ch, sh** and **x**, add **es**. For example:  patch  →  patches

For nouns ending in a consonant and **y**,
change the **y** to **i** and then add **es**. For example:  fairy  →  fairies

Some plurals do not follow a rule. For example:  woman  →  women
They are called **irregular plurals**.

Change each of the singular nouns in these sentences into plural nouns.
The first sentence has been done for you.

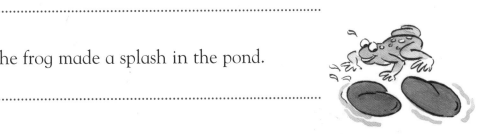

The dog chased the cat.

The dogs chased the cats.

The fairy granted the wish.

..................................................

The baby played with the toy.

..................................................

The frog made a splash in the pond.

..................................................

The boy played with the basketball.

..................................................

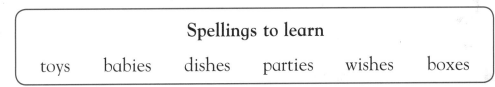

| Spellings to learn |
| --- |

toys    babies    dishes    parties    wishes    boxes

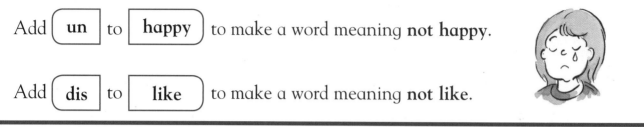

**FACTS**

A **prefix** is a group of letters that can be added to the beginning of a **root word** to change its meaning. For example: **un** and **dis** are prefixes meaning **not**.

Add [ **un** ] to [ **happy** ] to make a word meaning **not happy**.

Add [ **dis** ] to [ **like** ] to make a word meaning **not like**.

Use these prefixes **un** and **dis** to make the opposite of each of the words below.

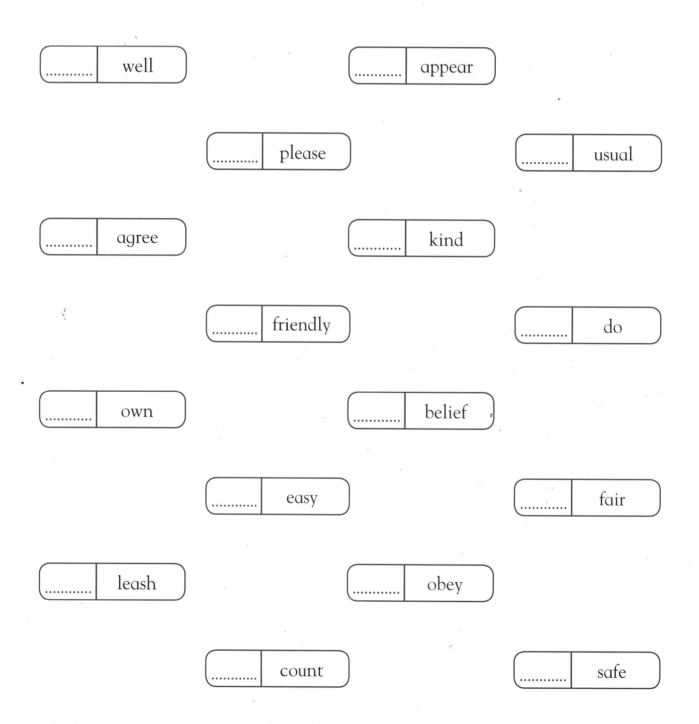

[............] well          [............] appear

[............] please          [............] usual

[............] agree          [............] kind

[............] friendly          [............] do

[............] own          [............] belief

[............] easy          [............] fair

[............] leash          [............] obey

[............] count          [............] safe

The prefix **pre** means **before**. For example:

| pre | + | fix | = | pre | fix |

A **prefix** is a group of letters added before a root word.

Fill in the missing letters in the following words, which all begin with **pre**.

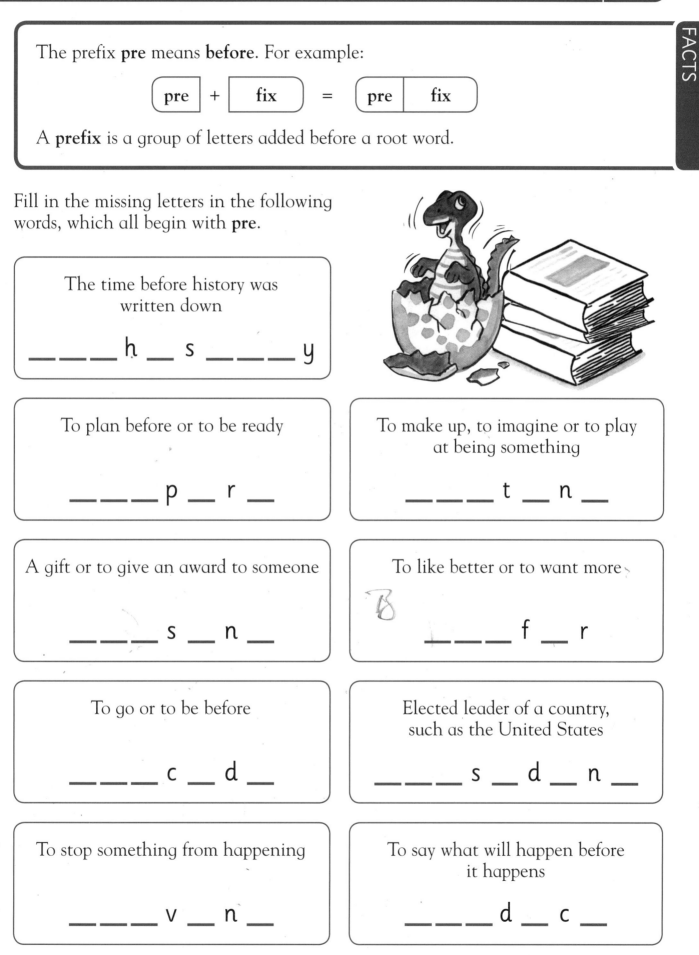

The time before history was written down

_ _ _ _ h _ s _ _ _ _ y

To plan before or to be ready

_ _ _ _ p _ r _

To make up, to imagine or to play at being something

_ _ _ _ t _ n _

A gift or to give an award to someone

_ _ _ _ s _ n _

To like better or to want more

_ _ _ _ f _ r

To go or to be before

_ _ _ _ c _ d _

Elected leader of a country, such as the United States

_ _ _ _ s _ d _ n _

To stop something from happening

_ _ _ _ v _ n _

To say what will happen before it happens

_ _ _ _ d _ c _

**FACTS**

The prefix **de** means **down, below** and **away from**. It can also change a **root word** to its opposite meaning.

Add the prefix **de** to complete the words on the notebook below.

...........stroy        ...........frost        ...........sign

...........cide         ...........feat         ...........scribe

...........pend         ...........ceive        ...........liver

...........crease       ...........scend        ...........posit

Complete the following sentences using the words above.

I can ........................... on my good friend.

Mark has to ........................... a parcel.

Try and ........................... what your house looks like.

Ben did not mean to ........................... Usha's toys.

We ........................... new equipment in technology.

The boy told a lie, trying to ........................... the teacher.

The car driver needed to ........................... her speed.

I can't ........................... which clothes to wear.

Gran had to ........................... the pizza from the freezer.

Ali went to ........................... the money in the bank.

Team A might ........................... team B in the match.

The aeroplane began to ........................... .

FACTS

The prefix **re** means **again**. **Recycle** means **to use something again**.

Read the words on the word bin. Pick eight words and write the prefix **re** in front of each one. One has been done for you.

**Word bin**

| | | |
|---|---|---|
| fuse | build | call |
| lease | visit | quest |
| place | write | turn |
| ward | mind | move |
| member | pay | fill |

refuse
...............................................................................
...............................................................................
...............................................................................
...............................................................................
...............................................................................
...............................................................................
...............................................................................

Use your new words in sentences of your own.

...............................................................................
...............................................................................
...............................................................................
...............................................................................
...............................................................................
...............................................................................
...............................................................................

# ★ Secret message

FACTS

A code can be used to write a secret message. Only people who know the code (or very clever people who can crack it) are able to decode and read the message.

|   | A | B | C |
|---|---|---|---|
| 1 | re | co | dis |
| 2 | pre | de | mis |
| 3 | ex | non | un |

Use the chart above to decode the secret message below.
For example: "Message (**C3**) clear" means "Message unclear" because (**C3**) = **un**.

If you (**B2**)........ cide to (**C3**)........ do this puzzle, you will need to

use the (**A2**)........ fix chart. (**A2**)........ pare to (**C1**)........ cover an

(**C3**)........ usual and (**A3**)........ citing mission. (**A3**)........ pose the

(**C3**)........ seen (**A2**)........ fixes in this message and then (**A1**)........ turn

to your base. Wear a (**C1**)........ guise. Don't make any (**C2**)........ takes.

(**A2**)........ pare for (**A3**)........ plosive action and (**B3**)........ -stop

adventure. Thanks for your (**B1**)........ operation.

| Spellings to learn | | | | | |
|---|---|---|---|---|---|
| dishonest | discover | unkind | prepare | design | remind |

FACTS

A **contraction** is two words joined together to make one word.
One or two letters are taken out.

For example:  I am ⟶ I'm

Join each of the following words to its contraction. One has been done for you.

| Words | | Contractions |

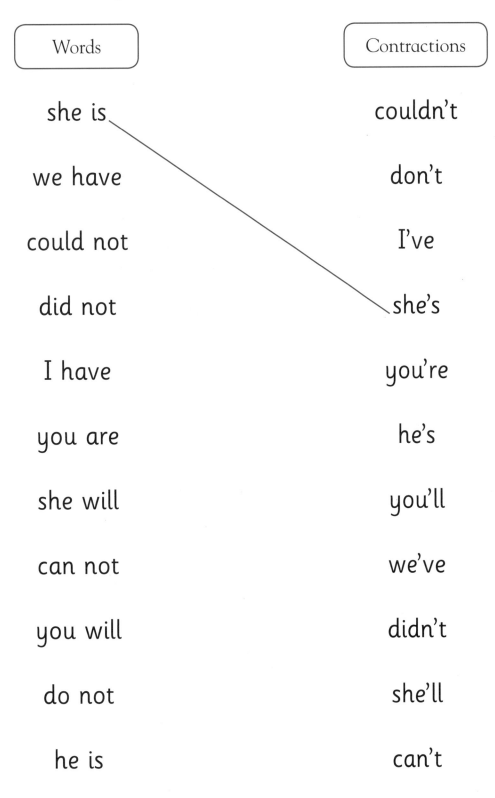

| she is | couldn't |
| we have | don't |
| could not | I've |
| did not | she's |
| I have | you're |
| you are | he's |
| she will | you'll |
| can not | we've |
| you will | didn't |
| do not | she'll |
| he is | can't |

Some words sound alike, or rhyme, even though their endings are spelled differently, as in **fight** and **kite**.

Read these words aloud.

| | | | | |
|---|---|---|---|---|
| creep | played | chew | plane | goal |
| bite | pain | pie | night | |
| made | hole | heap | fly | blue |

Find the rhyming pairs and write them in the boxes below. One pair has been done.

........... blue ...........     ........... chew ...........

Make some more rhyming pairs of your own.

FACTS

Words that rhyme help you write poems.

For each of the three words below, can you spell six rhyming words?
The picture clues may help you.

eye

blue

free

A **blend** is a combination of two or more consonants used together.
For example: the letters **g** and **r** are used together to make a blend in words such as **gr**owl, **gr**eet and **gr**asp.

gr  + owl  =  growl

Join the blends to the word ends below to make new words. Try to make at least 15 words.

| Blends | | | Word ends | | |
|---|---|---|---|---|---|
| gr | br | st | ow | op | ick |
| sl | tr | | im | ash | |
| cl | fl | cr | ab | ip | and |

........................................ ........................................ ........................................

........................................ ........................................ ........................................

........................................ ........................................ ........................................

........................................ ........................................ ........................................

........................................ ........................................ ........................................

**Silent letters** are the ones we do not pronounce.
For example: the **k** in **k**nife is not pronounced.

Read the sentences below. Look at the words set in bold. Cross out the silent letters in each of these words.

The **signpost** was bent **halfway** up.

The **honest knight knew** he needed a **sword**.

Lisa cut her **thumb** with a **knife** and went
**white** with shock.

I tried to stay **calm** but my **knees** were **knocking**.

We **wrote rhymes** about **gnats**.

Jan should **comb** her hair, but I **doubt** she does.

Now write each of these words on the correct line below. Can you think of other words with silent letters? Add your own words to the lists.

silent **l** ...............................................................................................

silent **k** ...............................................................................................

silent **g** ...............................................................................................

silent **w** ...............................................................................................

silent **h** ...............................................................................................

silent **b** ...............................................................................................

| Spellings to learn | | | | | | | |
|---|---|---|---|---|---|---|---|
| eight | rhymes | slow | doubt | honest | thumb | island | knew |

Solving a crossword is fun and a great way of learning new words. Once you fill in a few words, the answers to the rest of the clues become easier because you already have a few of their letters.

All the words in the crossword puzzle below end with the letters **le**. Read each of the clues and complete the crossword. Some letters are given to help you.

**Across**
1  To fidget
2  You use it to sew
3  90° is a right ...............
4  A mess or a mix up
5  ............... gum
6  Small or tiny
7  A round shape
8  E.g. means "for ..............."

**Down**
1  Disgusting or awful
2  To complain
3  A fruit
4  Polly, put the ............... on
5  Mum's brother
6  A four-legged piece of furniture
7  Something that is in the way
8  A cabbage is a ...............

Sometimes, short words can be found within long words without changing the letter order. For example, in **sometimes** you can find:

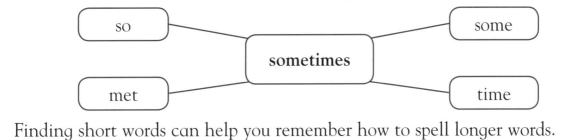

so

some

**sometimes**

met

time

Finding short words can help you remember how to spell longer words.

Find four short words in each of these long words.

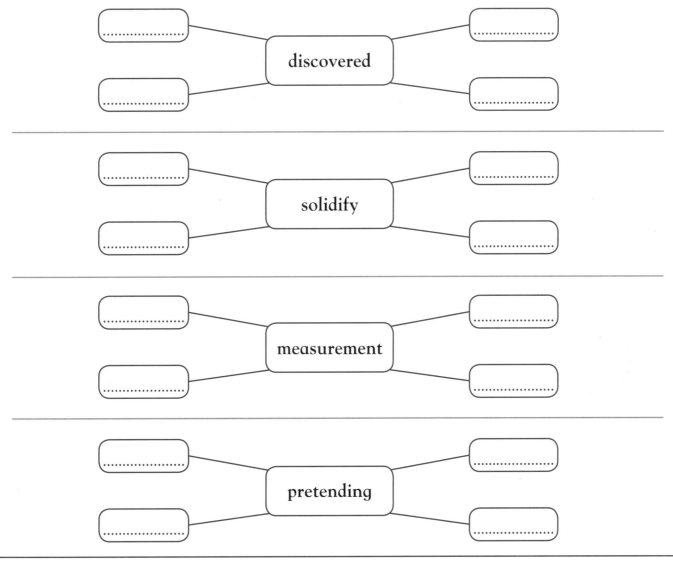

**discovered**

**solidify**

**measurement**

**pretending**

Can you find short words in the long words below? Write your answers on a separate piece of paper.

handwriting      transformation      theatre      frustration

# ★ Spelling practice

Writing out words is the best way to learn their spellings.

Look at the four words in each group. Now cover the words and write them in the second column. Then check your spellings and write the words again in the next column. Repeat the exercise using the third and fourth columns.

arrive
different
guide
minute

perhaps
surprise
centre
history

imagine
naughty
potatoes
thought

breathe
continue
grammar
regular

separate
certain
early
forwards

A **compound word** is formed by joining two short words together to make one longer word.

For example:     **day + light = daylight**

Combine short words from the first row with short words from the second row to make 20 compound words.

| no | play | grand | any | out | some | in | every | sun | day |
|---|---|---|---|---|---|---|---|---|---|
| light | father | body | thing | where | one | side | shine | time | mother |

.....................................   .....................................

.....................................   .....................................

.....................................   .....................................

.....................................   .....................................

.....................................   .....................................

.....................................   .....................................

.....................................   .....................................

.....................................   .....................................

.....................................   .....................................

.....................................   .....................................

Can you think of any other compound words?

.....................................   .....................................

.....................................   .....................................

.....................................   .....................................

.....................................   .....................................

Sometimes, the spelling of a root word changes when adding the letters **ing**.

For root words ending with the letter **e**, you usually drop the **e**.
For example:   make ⟶ making

For root words ending with a short vowel and a consonant,
you double the consonant.
For example:   stop ⟶ stopping

For other root words, you just add **ing**.
For example:   find ⟶ finding

In the first column, look at the word endings. In the second column, write out the rule for each group and then use it when adding **ing** to the root words in the last column (the first rule and one of the words have been done for you).

| Word endings | The rules | Add **ing** |
|---|---|---|
| Root words ending with the letter **e** | Drop the **e** and then add **ing**. .................................. .................................. | write ........ writing ........ <br> create .................................. <br> hide .................................. <br> lose .................................. |
| Root words ending with a short vowel and a consonant | .................................. .................................. .................................. .................................. | put .................................. <br> slip .................................. <br> sit .................................. <br> get .................................. |
| Root words ending in other letters | .................................. .................................. .................................. | draw .................................. <br> say .................................. <br> cook .................................. <br> tell .................................. |

There are a number of rules to remember when adding the letters **ing** to a root word.

Sometimes, **ing** is just added to the end of a word.
For example:     **shout + ing = shouting**

If the word ends in **e**, drop the **e** before adding **ing**.
For example:     **wave + ing = waving**

For a word with a short vowel sound before the last letter, double the last letter before adding **ing**.
For example:     **pop + ing = popping**

                 **hit + ing = hitting**

Add **ing** to these root words. Watch out for words with short vowel sounds (shown in bold).

scream ......................................        do ......................................

**run** ......................................        take ......................................

lose ......................................        play ......................................

**clap** ......................................        like ......................................

hope ......................................        **put** ......................................

go ......................................        stay ......................................

**stop** ......................................        ride ......................................

cry ......................................        help ......................................

# ★ | What are they doing?

Doing, or action, words are also called **verbs**.

Look at the pictures and write answers to the following questions. Use the rules for adding **ing** to root words. One has been done for you.

What is the boy doing?

The boy is smiling.

What is the girl doing?

.........................................................................

What is the dog doing?

.........................................................................

What is the boy doing?

.........................................................................

What is the girl doing?

.........................................................................

What is the cat doing?

.........................................................................

What is the monkey doing?

.........................................................................

What is the teacher doing?

.........................................................................

| Spellings to learn | | | | | |
|---|---|---|---|---|---|
| starting | making | something | chasing | stopping | putting |

FACTS

There are three rules to remember when making **adjectives** by adding **y** to nouns.

If the root word ends in a short vowel and a consonant, double the last letter before adding **y**.

For example:  **fun** + **y**  =  **funny**

If the root word ends in **e**, drop the **e** before adding **y**.

For example:  **spice** + **y**  =  **spicy**

For other nouns, just add **y**.

For example:  **mess** + **y**  =  **messy**

Add **y** to each of the root words below to make an adjective. Then use the adjective to describe something. One has been done for you.

| Root words | Adjective | Describe something |
|---|---|---|
| sun | sunny | sunny skies |
| ice | | |
| run | | |
| fog | | |
| smoke | | |
| sand | | |
| stick | | |
| noise | | |

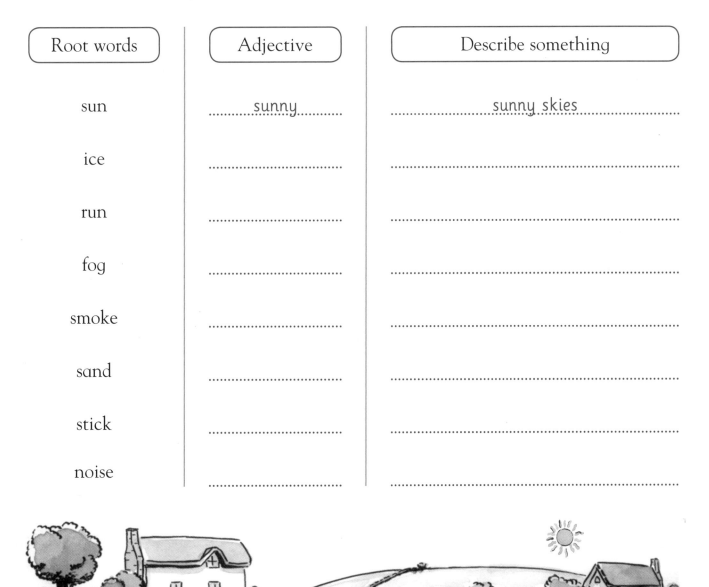

An **adverb** is a word that describes a **verb**. It describes how an action is done. For example: in the sentence **Jill walked slowly**, the word **slowly** is an adverb as it describes how Jill walked.

**Remember**: a verb is a doing, or action, word.

Add **ly** to these words to make adverbs.

brave ...........................................          slow ...........................................

quiet ...........................................          sad ...........................................

quick ...........................................          loud ...........................................

real ...........................................          careful ...........................................

Choose the correct words from the new words you have made above to complete these sentences.

We listened ........................ to the bad news.

Our teacher said, "Shh! Talk ........................."

The knight fought ........................ against the giant.

The pop group played .........................

We carried the baby .........................

I ........................ enjoyed my tea.

The fire spread .........................

The snail moved .........................

FACTS

A **suffix** is a group of letters that can be added to the end of a root word to change its meaning.

For example:  **tall + er = taller**

**tall + est = tallest**

Join each of the root words below to its **er** and **est** forms.
One has been done for you.

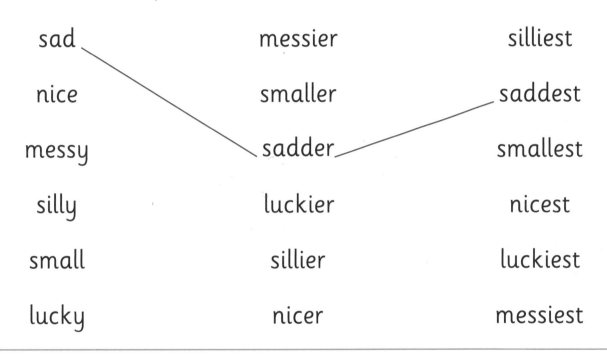

| sad | messier | silliest |
| nice | smaller | saddest |
| messy | sadder | smallest |
| silly | luckier | nicest |
| small | sillier | luckiest |
| lucky | nicer | messiest |

Now sort the words into the following three columns.

| Root words | er suffix | est suffix |
|---|---|---|
| .................. | .................. | .................. |
| .................. | .................. | .................. |
| .................. | .................. | .................. |
| .................. | .................. | .................. |
| .................. | .................. | .................. |
| .................. | .................. | .................. |

FACTS

When adding the suffix **er** or **est** to root words, you should drop the **e** if the root word already ends in **e**. For example:  nice ⟶ **nicer**

safe ⟶ **safest**

For root words ending in a short vowel and a consonant, double the consonant and add **er** or **est**. For example:  hot ⟶ **hotter**

wet ⟶ **wettest**

For root words ending in a consonant and **y**, change the **y** to **i** and add **er** or **est**. For example:  happy ⟶ **happier**

silly ⟶ **silliest**

In the first column, look at the word endings. In the second column, write out the rule for each group and then use it when adding **er** and **est** to the root words in the last column (the first rule and one of the words have been done for you).

| Word endings | The rules | Add er and est | | |
|---|---|---|---|---|
| Root words ending with the letter e | Drop the **e** and add **er** or **est**. | late | later | latest |
| | | pure | | |
| | | tame | | |
| | | white | | |
| | | brave | | |
| Root words ending with a short vowel and a consonant | | big | | |
| | | fit | | |
| | | fat | | |
| | | sad | | |
| | | thin | | |
| Root words ending with a consonant and y | | messy | | |
| | | lucky | | |
| | | trendy | | |
| | | nasty | | |
| | | musty | | |

# The suffixes "ful" and "less" ⭐

The suffixes **ful** and **less** can be added to root words to make new words.
The suffix **ful** means **full of** and the suffix **less** means **without**.
**Remember:** ful is like the word **full** but with just one **l**.

For example:  **cheer  +  ful   =  cheerful**

**fear  +  less  =  fearless**

Add either **ful** or **less** to each of these root words to make new words.

| Root words | New words |
| --- | --- |
| spot | ................................................................ |
| success | ................................................................ |
| breath | ................................................................ |
| help | ................................................................ |
| fear | ................................................................ |
| care | ................................................................ |

Use the new words above to write six sentences of your own.

................................................................................................................

................................................................................................................

................................................................................................................

................................................................................................................

................................................................................................................

................................................................................................................

# ★ More about "ful" and "less"

FACTS

When adding a **suffix** to a **root word**, a new word is made. The new word may be used to replace several other words.

For example: **careful** means **full of care** and **careless** means **without care**.

Rewrite each of these sentences using one word for the words in bold.

The children were **full of cheer** at the party.

...................................................................................................

Lindsay was **full of care** with her spelling.

...................................................................................................

My snapped pencil is **without use**.

...................................................................................................

By half-time, the match was **without hope**.

...................................................................................................

The sunset was **full of wonder**.

...................................................................................................

My injection was completely **without pain**.

...................................................................................................

We were **without speech** as we listened to the choir.

...................................................................................................

My tooth was **full of pain**.

...................................................................................................

FACTS

If a root word ends with a short vowel and a consonant, double the last letter before you add the suffix.

If a root word ends in **e**, drop the **e** before adding the suffix.

Make new words by adding the suffixes in the box below to the following root words. Can you make at least two new words from each root word?

| er | est | ful | less | ly | ing |
|----|-----|-----|------|----|----|

use ..... *useless*

soft ..... *soft softer*

hope ..... *hopeful*

loud ..... *loudest*

hot ..... *hotter*

care ..... *careful*

play ..... *playing*

close ..... *close closing*

thank .....

friend .....

shop .....

# ★ More spelling practice

Writing out words many times is a great way to memorise their spellings.

Look at the four words in each group. Now cover the words and write them in the second column. Then check your spellings and write the words again in the next column. Repeat the exercise using the third and fourth columns.

often ......................... ......................... ......................... .........................

answer ......................... ......................... ......................... .........................

build ......................... ......................... ......................... .........................

calendar ......................... ......................... ......................... .........................

centre ......................... ......................... ......................... .........................

notice ......................... ......................... ......................... .........................

various ......................... ......................... ......................... .........................

strength ......................... ......................... ......................... .........................

appear ......................... ......................... ......................... .........................

difficult ......................... ......................... ......................... .........................

guard ......................... ......................... ......................... .........................

library ......................... ......................... ......................... .........................

learn ......................... ......................... ......................... .........................

quarter ......................... ......................... ......................... .........................

probably ......................... ......................... ......................... .........................

strange ......................... ......................... ......................... .........................

address ......................... ......................... ......................... .........................

earth ......................... ......................... ......................... .........................

knowledge ......................... ......................... ......................... .........................

therefore ......................... ......................... ......................... .........................

# Answer section with parents' notes

## Key Stage 2
## Ages 7–8

This eight-page section provides answers and explanatory notes to all the activities in this book, enabling you to assess your child's work.

Work through each page together and ensure that your child understands each task. Point out any mistakes your child makes and correct any errors in spelling. (Your child should use the handwriting style taught at his or her school.) As well as making corrections, it is very important to praise your child's efforts and achievements.

At the end of this section, there is a glossary that includes all the key terms covered in this book.

---

**4** ★ Find the plurals

When there is one of something, we say it is **singular**.
For example: Tom had one **apple** for breakfast.

When there is more than one of something, we say it is **plural**.
For example: Tom had two **apples** for breakfast.

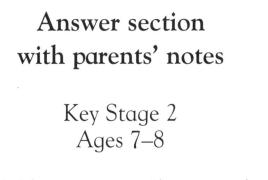

apple        apples

Join each of the singular words below to its plural. One has been done for you.

| Singular | Plural |
|---|---|
| light | dresses |
| bicycle | lights |
| baby | journeys |
| watch | torches |
| dress | babies |
| country | exercises |
| journey | watches |
| boy | days |
| fly | bicycles |
| torch | centuries |
| bus | trays |
| exercise | boys |
| day | flies |
| century | countries |
| shoe | buses |
| tray | shoes |

In this matching activity, your child needs to find the plurals for the words. Go through the page with him or her first, reading the singular and plural words in a random order.

---

**5** Find the rule ★

The **plurals** of words ending in **soft sounds**, such as **s, ss, sh, ch** and **x** have **es** at the end.
For example:    box  →  boxes

Make plurals of words ending in a **vowel** and **y** by adding **s**.
For example:    toy  →  toys

For plurals of words ending in a **consonant** and **y**, change the **y** to **i** and add **es**.
For example:    jelly  →  jellies

Look at the word endings in the first column below. In the second column, write out the rule for making plurals for each group and then use it to make the words in the last column plural (the first rule and one of the examples have been done for you).

fishes! fishyes! fishes! fishies! fish!

| Word endings | The rules | Examples | |
|---|---|---|---|
| s, ss, sh, ch and x | Add **es** to the end. | dish | dishes |
| | | match | matches |
| | | fox | foxes |
| A vowel and y | Add **s** to the end. | donkey | donkeys |
| | | boy | boys |
| | | way | ways |
| A consonant and y | Change **y** to **i** and add **es**. | granny | grannies |
| | | potty | potties |
| | | party | parties |

Understanding how spelling rules operate on certain words helps children remember them. Your child should look at how the words are changed and then write the rules in his or her own words.

---

**6** ★ Singular to plural

A **singular** word describes just one thing, such as one car, but a **plural** can be any amount greater than one, such as two, fifty or one million cars.

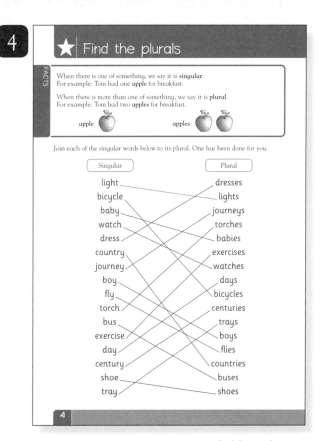

car        cars

Change the singular words to plural and the plural words to singular.

| Singular | Plural |
|---|---|
| hiss | hisses |
| party | parties |
| dish | dishes |
| word | words |
| group | groups |
| bush | bushes |
| country | countries |
| watch | watches |
| tray | trays |
| donkey | donkeys |
| butterfly | butterflies |
| monkey | monkeys |
| heart | hearts |

In this activity, your child looks at and listens to the differences between the endings of singular and plural nouns. He or she may need to refer to the plural spelling rules on page 5.

## Making plurals ★

To make **singular** nouns into **plurals**, the word endings are changed.

For most nouns, just add **s**. For example:  cat  →  cats

For nouns ending in soft sounds, such as
**s, ss, ch, sh** and **x**, add **es**. For example: patch  →  patches

For nouns ending in a consonant and **y**,
change the **y** to **i** and then add **es**. For example: fairy  →  fairies

Some plurals do not follow a rule. For example: woman  →  women
They are called **irregular plurals**.

Change each of the singular nouns in these sentences into plural nouns.
The first sentence has been done for you.

The dog chased the cat.
The dogs chased the cats.

The fairy granted the wish.
The fairies granted the wishes.

The baby played with the toy.
The babies played with the toys.

The frog made a splash in the pond.
The frogs made splashes in the ponds.

The boy played with the basketball.
The boys played with the basketballs.

**Spellings to learn**
toys   babies   dishes   parties   wishes   boxes

In this activity, some of the basic rules for making plural nouns are reinforced. The endings **s**, **ss**, **sh**, **ch** and **x** also include **tch** (as in sti**tch**es) and are sometimes described as soft endings.

---

## ★ The prefixes "un" and "dis"

A **prefix** is a group of letters that can be added to the beginning of a **root word** to change its meaning. For example: **un** and **dis** are prefixes meaning **not**.

Add  un  to  happy  to make a word meaning **not happy**.

Add  dis  to  like  to make a word meaning **not like**.

Use these prefixes **un** and **dis** to make the opposite of each of the words below.

un well          dis appear

dis please          un usual

dis agree          un kind

un friendly          un do

dis own          dis belief

un easy          un fair

un leash          dis obey

dis count          un safe

To decide which prefix to use, your child could try saying the word with each prefix and then think about which one sounds right. Encourage your child to check his or her answers in a dictionary.

---

## The prefix "pre" ★

The prefix **pre** means **before**. For example:

pre + fix = pre fix

A **prefix** is a group of letters added before a root word.

Fill in the missing letters in the following words, which all begin with **pre**.

The time before history was written down
p r e h i s t o r y

To plan before or to be ready
p r e p a r e

To make up, to imagine or to play at being something
p r e t e n d

A gift or to give an award to someone
p r e s e n t

To like better or to want more
p r e f e r

To go or to be before
p r e c e d e

Elected leader of a country, such as the United States
p r e s i d e n t

To stop something from happening
p r e v e n t

To say what will happen before it happens
p r e d i c t

Your child needs to read each definition and consider which word beginning with **pre** it describes. Before starting, your child may find it helpful to think of words that begin with **pre**.

---

## ★ The prefix "de"

The prefix **de** means **down, below** and **away from**. It can also change a **root word** to its opposite meaning.

Add the prefix **de** to complete the words on the notebook below.

| | | |
|---|---|---|
| destroy | defrost | design |
| decide | defeat | describe |
| depend | deceive | deliver |
| decrease | descend | deposit |

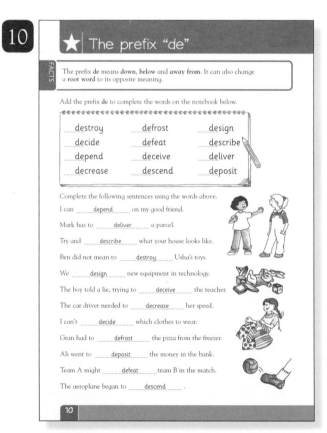

Complete the following sentences using the words above.

I can ____depend____ on my good friend.

Mark has to ____deliver____ a parcel.

Try and ____describe____ what your house looks like.

Ben did not mean to ____destroy____ Usha's toys.

We ____design____ new equipment in technology.

The boy told a lie, trying to ____deceive____ the teacher.

The car driver needed to ____decrease____ her speed.

I can't ____decide____ which clothes to wear.

Gran had to ____defrost____ the pizza from the freezer.

Ali went to ____deposit____ the money in the bank.

Team A might ____defeat____ team B in the match.

The aeroplane began to ____descend____ .

By adding the **de** prefix to these roots, your child will make words he or she recognises. Encourage him or her to read the roots before adding the prefix and then learn the words.

## Recycling words ★

FACTS

The prefix **re** means **again**. **Recycle** means **to use something again**.

Read the words on the word bin. Pick eight words and write the prefix **re** in front of each one. One has been done for you.

re_refuse

**Word bin**

| | | |
|---|---|---|
| fuse | build | call |
| lease | visit | quest |
| place | write | turn |
| ward | mind | move |
| member | pay | fill |

*Answers may vary*

Use your new words in sentences of your own.

*Answers may vary*

11

The root words in the word bin are all complete words. Your child can use this activity to compare the original meaning of the root word with the new word formed by adding the prefix **re**.

---

## ★ Secret message

FACTS

A code can be used to write a secret message. Only people who know the code (or very clever people who can crack it) are able to decode and read the message.

| | A | B | C |
|---|---|---|---|
| 1 | re | co | dis |
| 2 | pre | de | mis |
| 3 | ex | non | un |

Use the chart above to decode the secret message below.
For example: "Message (C3) clear" means "Message unclear" because (C3) = **un**.

If you (B2) _de_ cide to (C3) _un_ do this puzzle, you will need to use the (A2) _pre_ fix chart. (A2) _Pre_ pare to (C1) _dis_ cover an (C3) _un_ usual and (A3) _ex_ citing mission. (A3) _Ex_ pose the (C3) _un_ seen (A2) _pre_ fixes in this message and then (A1) _re_ turn to your base. Wear a (C1) _dis_ guise. Don't make any (C2) _mis_ takes. (A2) _Pre_ pare for (A3) _ex_ plosive action and (B3) _non_ -stop adventure. Thanks for your (B1) _co_ operation.

| | **Spellings to learn** | | | | |
|---|---|---|---|---|---|
| dishonest | discover | unkind | prepare | design | remind |

12

Your child may guess the prefix needed to complete a code word and use the chart to check his or her answer. Your child could write his or her own secret message, using words beginning with the prefixes in the chart.

---

## Contractions ★

FACTS

A **contraction** is two words joined together to make one word.
One or two letters are taken out.
For example:  I am → I'm

Join each of the following words to its contraction. One has been done for you.

| Words | Contractions |
|---|---|
| she is | couldn't |
| we have | don't |
| could not | I've |
| did not | she's |
| I have | you're |
| you are | he's |
| she will | you'll |
| can not | we've |
| you will | didn't |
| do not | she'll |
| he is | can't |

13

Your child needs to remember how the apostrophe is used and where it is positioned in contractions. Point out that the apostrophe in **I'm** replaces the **a** in the **am** of **I am**.

---

## ★ Rhyming pairs

FACTS

Some words sound alike, or rhyme, even though their endings are spelled differently, as in **fight** and **kite**.

Read these words aloud.

| | | | | |
|---|---|---|---|---|
| creep | played | chew | plane | goal |
| bite | pain | pie | night | |
| made | hole | heap | fly | blue |

Find the rhyming pairs and write them in the boxes below. One pair has been done.

| blue | chew |
|---|---|

| creep | heap | | pain | plane |
|---|---|---|---|---|
| played | made | | hole | goal |
| bite | night | | pie | fly |

Make some more rhyming pairs of your own.

*Answers may vary*

14

Here, your child identifies some common ways in which long vowel sounds are made with different spelling patterns, such as the long **o** sound in **hole** and **goal**. Encourage your child to learn these spelling patterns.

## Rhyme time ⭐

FACTS

Words that rhyme help you write poems.

For each of the three words below, can you spell six rhyming words?
The picture clues may help you. **Answers may vary**

**eye**

| | |
|---|---|
| tie | cry |
| fly | sky |
| pie | high |

**blue**

| | |
|---|---|
| glue | two |
| flew | moo |
| through | shoe |

**free**

| | |
|---|---|
| three | knee |
| sea | tree |
| tea | pea |

Encourage your child to think of his or her
own suggestions for rhyming words, rather
than only using the picture clues. The clues
can be used to prompt answers when necessary.

---

## ⭐ Blends and ends

FACTS

A **blend** is a combination of two or more consonants used together.
For example: the letters **g** and **r** are used together to make a blend in words
such as **gr**owl, **gr**eet and **gr**asp.

gr + owl = growl

Join the blends to the word ends below to make new words. Try to make at least
15 words.

| Blends | | | Word ends | | |
|---|---|---|---|---|---|
| gr | br | st | ow | op | ick |
| sl | tr | | im | ash | |
| cl | fl | cr | ab | ip | and |

*Answers may vary*

Blends of two or more consonant sounds are
often used in words. Although individual
sounds can be identified, they run together
smoothly in a blend, such as **bl** in the words
**bl**ack and **bl**ue.

---

## Silent letters ⭐

FACTS

**Silent letters** are the ones we do not pronounce.
For example: the **k** in knife is not pronounced.

Read the sentences below. Look at the words set in bold. Cross out the silent letters
in each of these words.

The **signpost** was bent **halfway** up.

The **honest knight knew** he needed a **sword**.

Lisa cut her **thumb** with a **knife** and went
**white** with shock.

I tried to stay **calm** but my **knees** were **knocking**.

We **wrote** r**h**ymes about **gnats**.

Jan should **comb** her hair, but I **doubt** she does.

Now write each of these words on the correct line below. Can you think of other
words with silent letters? Add your own words to the lists.

| | |
|---|---|
| silent l | halfway   calm |
| silent k | knight   knew   knees   knocking   knife |
| silent g | gnats   signpost |
| silent w | wrote   sword |
| silent h | honest   rhymes   white |
| silent b | thumb   comb   doubt |

**Spellings to learn**

eight   rhymes   slow   doubt   honest   thumb   island   knew

Help your child identify the letter that can't
be heard by encouraging him or her to look
closely at each bold word while saying it aloud.
Breaking up the word into its letter sounds
will also help identify the silent letters.

---

## ⭐ The "le" crossword

FACTS

Solving a crossword is fun and a great way of learning new words. Once you
fill in a few words, the answers to the rest of the clues become easier because
you already have a few of their letters.

All the words in the crossword puzzle below end with the letters **le**. Read each
of the clues and complete the crossword. Some letters are given to help you.

| Across | Down |
|---|---|
| 1 To fidget | 1 Disgusting or awful |
| 2 You use it to sew | 2 To complain |
| 3 90° is a right .............. | 3 A fruit |
| 4 A mess or a mix up | 4 Polly, put the .............. on |
| 5 .............. gum | 5 Mum's brother |
| 6 Small or tiny | 6 A four-legged piece of furniture |
| 7 A round shape | 7 Something that is in the way |
| 8 E.g. means "for .............." | 8 A cabbage is a .............. |

Crossword answers:
Across: 1 wriggle, 2 needle, 3 angle, 4 muddle, 5 bubble, 6 little, 7 circle, 8 example
Down: 1 horrible, 2 grumble, 3 apple, 4 kettle, 5 uncle, 6 table, 7 obstacle, 8 vegetable

Crosswords develop the skill of fitting spelling
patterns together in response to a set of clues.
Encourage your child to leave any clues he or
she is stuck on and come back to them later.

# Words in words ★

FACTS

Sometimes, short words can be found within long words without changing the letter order. For example, in **sometimes** you can find:

| so | | some |
|---|---|---|
| | **sometimes** | |
| met | | time |

Finding short words can help you remember how to spell longer words.

Find four short words in each of these long words. **Answers may vary**

| discover | | red |
|---|---|---|
| | **discovered** | |
| cover | | disco |

| solid | | so |
|---|---|---|
| | **solidify** | |
| lid | | if |

| measure | | as |
|---|---|---|
| | **measurement** | |
| sure | | me |

| pretend | | end |
|---|---|---|
| | **pretending** | |
| tend | | ending |

Can you find short words in the long words below? Write your answers on a separate piece of paper.

handwriting    transformation    theatre    frustration

Visual recognition of words and their spellings is particularly useful when your child needs to spell long words or words that do not follow conventional spelling rules.

---

# ★ Spelling practice

FACTS

Writing out words is the best way to learn their spellings.

Look at the four words in each group. Now cover the words and write them in the second column. Then check your spellings and write the words again in the next column. Repeat the exercise using the third and fourth columns.

| | | | | |
|---|---|---|---|---|
| arrive | arrive | arrive | arrive | arrive |
| different | different | different | different | different |
| guide | guide | guide | guide | guide |
| minute | minute | minute | minute | minute |
| perhaps | perhaps | perhaps | perhaps | perhaps |
| surprise | surprise | surprise | surprise | surprise |
| centre | centre | centre | centre | centre |
| history | history | history | history | history |
| imagine | imagine | imagine | imagine | imagine |
| naughty | naughty | naughty | naughty | naughty |
| potatoes | potatoes | potatoes | potatoes | potatoes |
| thought | thought | thought | thought | thought |
| breathe | breathe | breathe | breathe | breathe |
| continue | continue | continue | continue | continue |
| grammar | grammar | grammar | grammar | grammar |
| regular | regular | regular | regular | regular |
| separate | separate | separate | separate | separate |
| certain | certain | certain | certain | certain |
| early | early | early | early | early |
| forwards | forwards | forwards | forwards | forwards |

Encourage your child to complete carefully the Look, Say, Cover, Write and Check activity. Writing out the words repeatedly will imprint their spellings on your child's mind.

---

# Compound words ★

FACTS

A **compound word** is formed by joining two short words together to make one longer word.

For example:    **day + light = daylight**

Combine short words from the first row with short words from the second row to make 20 compound words.

| no | play | grand | any | out | some | in | every | sun | day |
|---|---|---|---|---|---|---|---|---|---|
| light | father | body | thing | where | one | side | shine | time | mother |

*Answers may vary*

Can you think of any other compound words?

*Answers may vary*

Compound words are made up of two small words, such as **anything**. Your child should realise that if he or she can spell the two small words, then he or she can spell the compound word.

---

# ★ Find the rule

FACTS

Sometimes, the spelling of a root word changes when adding the letters **ing**.

For root words ending with the letter **e**, you usually drop the **e**.

For example:   **make → making**

For root words ending with a short vowel and a consonant, you double the consonant.

For example:   **stop → stopping**

For other root words, you just add **ing**.

For example:   **find → finding**

In the first column, look at the word endings. In the second column, write out the rule for each group and then use it when adding **ing** to the root words in the last column (the first rule and one of the words have been done for you).

| Word endings | The rules | Add ing | |
|---|---|---|---|
| Root words ending with the letter **e** | Drop the **e** and then add **ing**. | write | writing |
| | | create | creating |
| | | hide | hiding |
| | | lose | losing |
| Root words ending with a short vowel and a consonant | Double the last consonant and add **ing**. | put | putting |
| | | slip | slipping |
| | | sit | sitting |
| | | get | getting |
| Root words ending in other letters | Add **ing** to the whole word. | draw | drawing |
| | | say | saying |
| | | cook | cooking |
| | | tell | telling |

Talk through the changes made to the words and encourage your child to apply the rules in his or her own writing.

## Add "ing"

FACTS

There are a number of rules to remember when adding the letters **ing** to a root word.

Sometimes, **ing** is just added to the end of a word.
For example: **shout** + **ing** = **shouting**

If the word ends in **e**, drop the **e** before adding **ing**.
For example: **wave** + **ing** = **waving**

For a word with a short vowel sound before the last letter, double the last letter before adding **ing**.
For example: **pop** + **ing** = **popping**
**hit** + **ing** = **hitting**

Add **ing** to these root words. Watch out for words with short vowel sounds (shown in bold).

| | | | |
|---|---|---|---|
| scream | screaming | do | doing |
| run | running | take | taking |
| lose | losing | play | playing |
| clap | clapping | like | liking |
| hope | hoping | put | putting |
| go | going | stay | staying |
| stop | stopping | ride | riding |
| cry | crying | help | helping |

23

The vowels are often taught by saying the letter names. One way of reinforcing the idea of the short vowel is for your child to say the vowels in their short sound form, for example, saying **a** as in **clap**.

---

## What are they doing?

FACTS

Doing, or action, words are also called **verbs**.

Look at the pictures and write answers to the following questions. Use the rules for adding **ing** to root words. One has been done for you.

What is the boy doing?
The boy is smiling.

What is the girl doing?
The girl is running.

What is the dog doing?
The dog is barking.

What is the boy doing?
The boy is singing.

What is the girl doing?
The girl is crying.

What is the cat doing?
The cat is purring.

What is the monkey doing?
The monkey is climbing.

What is the teacher doing?
The teacher is writing.

| Spellings to learn | | | | | |
|---|---|---|---|---|---|
| starting | making | something | chasing | stopping | putting |

24

As your child makes the various verbs needed in the answers, he or she should be aware of the **e** ending and the short vowel and consonant ending looked at on earlier pages.

---

## Adjectives with "y" endings

FACTS

There are three rules to remember when making **adjectives** by adding **y** to nouns.

If the root word ends in a short vowel and a consonant, double the last letter before adding **y**.
For example: **fun** + **y** = **funny**

If the root word ends in **e**, drop the **e** before adding **y**.
For example: **spice** + **y** = **spicy**

For other nouns, just add **y**.
For example: **mess** + **y** = **messy**

Add **y** to each of the root words below to make an adjective. Then use the adjective to describe something. One has been done for you.

| Root words | Adjective | Describe something |
|---|---|---|
| sun | sunny | sunny skies |
| ice | icy | |
| run | runny | |
| fog | foggy | *Answers may vary* |
| smoke | smoky | |
| sand | sandy | |
| stick | sticky | |
| noise | noisy | |

25

Point out that the rules for adding the suffix **y** are similar to those for adding the suffix **ing**. Once your child is familiar with the rules, he or she will be able to make descriptive words by adding the suffix **y**.

---

## Adverbs ending in "ly"

FACTS

An **adverb** is a word that describes a **verb**. It describes how an action is done. For example: in the sentence **Jill walked slowly**, the word **slowly** is an adverb as it describes how Jill walked.
**Remember:** a verb is a doing, or action, word.

Add **ly** to these words to make adverbs.

| | | | |
|---|---|---|---|
| brave | bravely | slow | slowly |
| quiet | quietly | sad | sadly |
| quick | quickly | loud | loudly |
| real | really | careful | carefully |

Choose the correct words from the new words you have made above to complete these sentences.

We listened ___sadly___ to the bad news.

Our teacher said, "Shh! Talk ___quietly___."

The knight fought ___bravely___ against the giant.

The pop group played ___loudly___.

We carried the baby ___carefully___.

I ___really___ enjoyed my tea.

The fire spread ___quickly___.

The snail moved ___slowly___.

26

To complete the sentences, your child will need to think about each adverb and then of the action it could describe.

## The suffixes "er" and "est" ★

FACTS

A **suffix** is a group of letters that can be added to the end of a root word to change its meaning.
For example: tall + er = taller
tall + est = tallest

Join each of the root words below to its **er** and **est** forms.
One has been done for you.

sad · messier · silliest
nice · smaller · saddest
messy · sadder · smallest
silly · luckier · nicest
small · sillier · luckiest
lucky · nicer · messiest

Now sort the words into the following three columns.

| Root words | er suffix | est suffix |
|---|---|---|
| sad | sadder | saddest |
| small | smaller | smallest |
| nice | nicer | nicest |
| lucky | luckier | luckiest |
| messy | messier | messiest |
| silly | sillier | silliest |

27

The **er** form, called the comparative, is used when comparing two things. The **est** form, called the superlative, is used when comparing three or more things, "Tom is **taller** than Jill, but I am the **tallest**".

---

## ★ Find the rule

FACTS

When adding the suffix **er** or **est** to root words, you should drop the **e** if the root word already ends in **e**. For example: nice → nicer
safe → safest
For root words ending in a short vowel and a consonant, double the consonant and add **er** or **est**. For example: hot → hotter
wet → wettest
For root words ending in a consonant and **y**, change the **y** to **i** and add **er** or **est**.
For example: happy → happier
silly → silliest

In the first column, look at the word endings. In the second column, write out the rule for each group and then use it when adding **er** and **est** to the root words in the last column (the first rule and one of the words have been done for you).

| Word endings | The rules | Add er and est | | |
|---|---|---|---|---|
| Root words ending with the letter e | Drop the e and add er or est. | late | later | latest |
| | | pure | purer | purest |
| | | tame | tamer | tamest |
| | | white | whiter | whitest |
| | | brave | braver | bravest |
| Root words ending with a short vowel and a consonant | Double the last consonant and add er or est. | big | bigger | biggest |
| | | fit | fitter | fittest |
| | | fat | fatter | fattest |
| | | sad | sadder | saddest |
| | | thin | thinner | thinnest |
| Root words ending with a consonant and y | Change the y to an i and then add er or est. | messy | messier | messiest |
| | | lucky | luckier | luckiest |
| | | trendy | trendier | trendiest |
| | | nasty | nastier | nastiest |
| | | musty | mustier | mustiest |

28

In this activity, your child learns each spelling rule by working out how it operates on certain words. Encourage your child to then think about when to apply the rule for other words.

---

## The suffixes "ful" and "less" ★

FACTS

The suffixes **ful** and **less** can be added to root words to make new words. The suffix **ful** means **full of** and the suffix **less** means **without**.
**Remember: ful** is like the word **full** but with just one **l**.
For example: cheer + ful = cheerful
fear + less = fearless

Add either **ful** or **less** to each of these root words to make new words.
**Answers may vary**

| Root words | New words |
|---|---|
| spot | spotless |
| success | successful |
| breath | breathless |
| help | helpful or helpless |
| fear | fearful or fearless |
| care | careful or careless |

Use the new words above to write six sentences of your own.

*Answers may vary*

29

On this page, your child practises making words with the suffixes **ful** and **less**. Some roots are only used with one of the suffixes, others will take either. Remind your child about using the one **l** in **ful**.

---

## ★ More about "ful" and "less"

FACTS

When adding a **suffix** to a **root word**, a new word is made. The new word may be used to replace several other words.
For example: **careful** means **full of care** and **careless** means **without care**.

Rewrite each of these sentences using one word for the words in bold.

The children were **full of cheer** at the party.
The children were cheerful at the party.

Lindsay was **full of care** with her spelling.
Lindsay was careful with her spelling.

My snapped pencil is **without use**.
My snapped pencil is useless.

By half-time, the match was **without hope**.
By half-time, the match was hopeless.

The sunset was **full of wonder**.
The sunset was wonderful.

My injection was completely **without pain**.
My injection was completely painless.

We were **without speech** as we listened to the choir.
We were speechless as we listened to the choir.

My tooth was **full of pain**.
My tooth was painful.

30

This activity covers a range of **ful** and **less** words. Extend the activity by asking your child to think of other words that end in these suffixes, and to see how the **full of** and **without** definitions apply.

## Word-maker ★

If a root word ends with a short vowel and a consonant, double the last letter before you add the suffix.
If a root word ends in e, drop the e before adding the suffix.

Make new words by adding the suffixes in the box below to the following root words. Can you make at least two new words from each root word?

| er | est | ful | less | ly | ing |
|----|-----|-----|------|----|----|

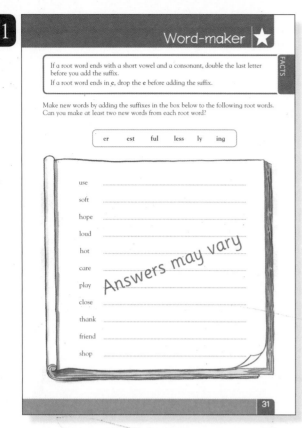

use

soft

hope

loud

hot

care

play

close

thank

friend

shop

*Answers may vary*

Your child is reminded of the ways in which suffixes can create new words. As he or she creates new words, you could ask him or her to say a sentence using each new word.

---

## ★ More spelling practice

Writing out words many times is a great way to memorise their spellings.

Look at the four words in each group. Now cover the words and write them in the second column. Then check your spellings and write the words again in the next column. Repeat the exercise using the third and fourth columns.

| | | | | |
|---|---|---|---|---|
| often | often | often | often | often |
| answer | answer | answer | answer | answer |
| build | build | build | build | build |
| calendar | calendar | calendar | calendar | calendar |
| centre | centre | centre | centre | centre |
| notice | notice | notice | notice | notice |
| various | various | various | various | various |
| strength | strength | strength | strength | strength |
| appear | appear | appear | appear | appear |
| difficult | difficult | difficult | difficult | difficult |
| guard | guard | guard | guard | guard |
| library | library | library | library | library |
| learn | learn | learn | learn | learn |
| quarter | quarter | quarter | quarter | quarter |
| probably | probably | probably | probably | probably |
| strange | strange | strange | strange | strange |
| address | address | address | address | address |
| earth | earth | earth | earth | earth |
| knowledge | knowledge | knowledge | knowledge | knowledge |
| therefore | therefore | therefore | therefore | therefore |

Ask your child to say sentences that include these words to show that he or she understands their meanings. For example: "I'll **probably** see my friend Alex tomorrow."

---

# Glossary

**Adjective**
A describing word, such as **big**, **blue** or **happy**.

**Adverb**
A word that describes a verb. For example: in **Katie sweetly sings**, **sweetly** is an adverb that describes the verb **sings**.

**Blend**
When two or more consonants are used together, such as **rk** in **dark**.

**Comparative**
The form of an adjective ending in **er**, such as **slower** or **smaller**.

**Compound word**
Two words put together to make one word, such as **skateboard**.

**Contraction**
When two words are joined to make one word. Missing letters are represented by an apostrophe. For example: **don't** (do not), **it's** (it is) and **you're** (you are).

**Homophones**
Words that sound the same but have different spellings and meanings, such as **stare** and **stair**.

**Irregular plurals**
Plurals that are not made by adding an **s** or **es** to the end of the singular. They include **mice** (mouse), **teeth** (tooth) and **children** (child).

**Plural**
More than one of something. We usually (but not always) add an **s** to the end of a singular noun to make it plural. For example: **desks**, **apples** and **horses**.

**Prefix**
A group of letters added to the front of a root word to change its meaning. Common prefixes include **de**, **re**, **in**, **un** and **dis**.

**Rhyming words**
Words that end in a similar sound, such as **park** and **bark**.

**Root word**
Form of a word without suffixes or prefixes. For example: **friend** is the root word of **friendly** and **befriend**.

**Silent letters**
Letters that are not pronounced in words, such as the **g** in **gnat** or the **h** in **whistle**.

**Singular**
Just one of something, such as a **cat** or a **train**.

**Suffix**
A group of letters added to the end of a root word to change its meaning or how it is used. Examples include **less** and **ful**.

**Superlative**
The form of an adjective ending in **est**, such as **fastest** or **biggest**.

**Verb**
A doing, or action, word, such as (to) **dance**, **smile** and **sleep**.